The fair is in town!
Mum tells Pip and Tim they can go. "But you
must not munch lots of sweets or you will be sick!"

The pair go to the fair. Pip wins things for
her hair. Tim wins lots and lots of sweets.
"Yum, yum," thinks Tim, as he starts to munch.

"Look!" Pip shouts, "Chairs in the air!"

Pip and Tim get on the chairs. They swing round and round. They swing high in the air.

"I feel sick," thinks Tim.

The chairs stop swinging. Pip and Tim get off. Tim rests near the chairs.

"Look!" yells Pip, "Hook-a-fish! Let's see if we can win." She drags Tim along.

Pip has a go.
She hooks a fish and wins a pair of socks!

Next, Tim has a go.

Tim wins a bag of sweets...
and a free trip on the Chairs in the air!

Speaking and listening

Who are these characters?

Pam   Pip   Tim

Can you read these words?

tie   coins   pool   rain

Spelling and writing

Ask your child to blend and read the words below. Ask them to say each word and to tap out the phonemes (sounds) of the word with their fingers. Then ask your child to try writing each word.

moan

statue

pure

Understanding the story

These questions will help you to check that your child understands the story.

1 Who goes to the fair? (page 1)

2 What does Mum say? (page 1)

3 Why does Tim feel sick? (page 5)